Self-Care
and
Comfort

ACTIVITY BOOK

for the
INNER
Pilgrimage

Welcome to this little book, it has been created to inspire you as you travel an inward journey of discovery, seeking to know yourself better and to nurture a closer walk with your Creator.

Included are prayers, meditations and activities to help you focus on your INNER Pilgrimage.

With every blessing,
Mary Fleeson, Holy Island.

The Flowing Tide

The flowing tide returns to the shore, it comes with the power of cleansing, washing away evidence of what has been and bringing home a mixture of bits and bobs that others have lost or discarded and on a tidal island like Lindisfarne it shrinks the land and create a true island.

For a while I want you to embrace the idea of being an island, allo yourself time to discover where you are in your relationship with Goc with your family and friends and who you have become as the year have passed by. Take a few deliberate steps with me on a God-centre inward journey, a pilgrimage of the heart and mind.

John 9.1-41

Dip your toes in!

Please dip in and out of this little book, it has been created to be used occasionally to accompany you on your daily pilgrim journey. Make notes in it, draw in it, colour in it, meditate on bits of it, enjoy it!

The following prayer could be used each time you use this book, think of it as an invitation to God to guide you and be beside you on your journey.

Be by my side Creator God,
Every step I take,
Be before me Saviour God,
Every step I take,
Be behind me Merciful God,
Every step I take,
Be within me strengthening God,
Every step I take.

The piece 'Be by my side' includes a simple map of Lindisfarne, a stylised dove representing the Holy Spirit, a shoreline and a Pilgrim Staff.

Be by my side Creator
Every step I take, GOD

Be before me Saviour
Every step I take, GOD

Be behind me Merciful
Every step I take, GOD

Be within me Strengthening
Every step I take, GOD

Self-care...

JESUS SAID, "COME WITH ME."

"COME WITH ME BY YOURSELVES TO A QUIET PLACE AND GET SOME REST." MARK 6:

"LOVE YOUR NEIGHBOUR AS YOURSELF." MARK 12:31

"ARE NOT FIVE SPARROWS SOLD FOR TWO PENNIES? YET NOT ONE OF THEM
FORGOTTEN BY GOD. INDEED, THE VERY HAIRS OF YOUR HEAD ARE ALL NUMBER
DON'T BE AFRAID; YOU ARE WORTH MORE THAN MANY SPARROWS." LUKE 12:6

The inward pilgrimage has the potential to be a difficult and painful one, but it doesn't have to be to gain a closer relationship with the God who created you. The journey may cause you to examine some deeply buried emotions, pre-concieved ideas and long-held beliefs - and that's okay, it's also okay if it doesn't dredge up any faith-challenging struggles. Looking after yourself includes understanding that the journey of faith will often be a gentle one filled with love, reassurances, treasured moments and peace, part of our self-care is to seek those moments and remember them so that when times are more challenging we can deliberately recall the positive experiences of our inner pilgrimage.

Recall the positive moments...

I felt loved when...

I felt reassured when...

One of my treasured moments was when...

I felt at peace when...

...and Comfort

PRAISE BE TO THE GOD AND FATHER OF OUR LORD JESUS CHRIST, THE FATHER OF COMPASSION AND THE GOD OF ALL COMFORT, WHO COMFORTS US IN ALL OUR TROUBLES, SO THAT WE CAN COMFORT THOSE IN ANY TROUBLE WITH THE COMFORT WE OURSELVES RECEIVE FROM GOD.
2 CORINTHIANS 1:3-4

PEACE I LEAVE WITH YOU; MY PEACE I GIVE YOU. I DO NOT GIVE TO YOU A THE WORLD GIVES. DO NOT LET YOUR HEARTS BE TROUBLED AND DO NOT AFRAID. JOHN 14:27

Grant me the faith to believe
That even when the path is hidd
You will show me Your way
When the time is right.

TOOLS FOR TRAVELLING

Everyone knows that it isn't wise or healthy to attribute too much power to physical things, we put our faith in God, end of story, but it doesn't hurt to use tools to help in our journeying. There are a few things that I like to use to enhance my prayer, meditation and inspiration times and I'd like to share two of them in the following pages...

The Holding Cross... these are often made of wood, smooth, ergonomically shaped and comfortable in the hand, or rough in texture and angular, challenging us to think about the pain of the true cross. A holding cross adds the dimension of touch to what may be an otherwise passive, cerebral experience of prayer.

Even if you have a holding cross you may like to try making your own following this simple pattern, you will need eight sheets of thick paper 7x20 cm and some yarn or string.

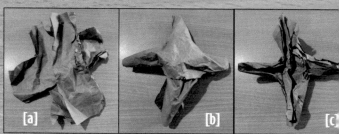

[a] [b] [c]

Lay the paper so that it makes a cross shape, first sheet up/down, next right/left [a]. Scrunch the paper so that one side is fairly smooth [b] (reverse [c]). Wrap yarn around until the paper is covered, tuck the ends of the cross arms in and finish by tucking in the end of the yarn.

...ditation... what does the cross say to you? Hold it tightly, notice the ...sion and strain in the muscles of your hand, let that tension move up ...r arm so that your muscles bunch, feel the ache in your shoulder and ...w it to spread to your back. As you grip the cross notice that it retains ...shape, it remains steadfast, still telling its story of forgiveness and ...emption.

...GIVENESS

...k of someone who has hurt you, deliberately or unintentionally, ...haps that hurt has been pushed down but never quite let go of... could ...be the time to forgive that person? If you are able to, say this prayer:

> Creator God, as You forgave me for the things I have done
> to hurt You, help me to forgive [name].
> Grant me the grace to release the pain and bad memories
> into Your care so that I may be free.

...EMPTION

...k of a situation that
...s without hope.
...his prayer:

> Loving God, Your
> sacrifice redeemed
> us so that we may
> know the freedom
> of life in Your
> presence.
> I ask for Your power
> to bring hope to
> [situation].
> Grant me the wisdom
> to know how to help.

Now release your grip on the cross, let it rest in your hand without any pressure, relax your body, breathe slowly and close your eyes. The cross your hand represents the promises of your faith; your prayers are hear your love will never be wasted, your life is precious and worth celebratin you are not alone.

AND I WILL ASK THE
FATHER, AND HE WILL
GIVE YOU ANOTHER
ADVOCATE TO HELP
YOU AND BE WITH
YOU FOREVER - THE
SPIRIT OF TRUTH
THE WORLD CANNOT
ACCEPT HIM
BECAUSE IT NEITHER
SEES HIM NOR KNOWS
HIM. BUT YOU KNOW
HIM, FOR HE LIVES
WITH YOU AND WIL
BE IN YOU

JOHN 14:16-17

Pilgrim staff... living in a place often visited by pilgrims I have been inspired to discover some interesting traditions practised around the world. One of my favourites is the idea of a pilgrim staff, a wooden walking stick used for centuries by pilgrims to help them walk safely on uneven ground, defend against attackers (at least in medieval times!) and even to help make a shelter.

The inspiration for the staffs I have made came from the Pilgrim Posts that lead to the Island across the sands, I created them from driftwood and attached shells, crinoids and sea glass. When meditating on them I am reminded of the shoreline, my go-to place to find some inner peace and reminders of the vastness of God, time and space. As each grain of sand is unique I remember the uniqueness of each person, as the tide ebbs and flows I remember that for every time I feel alone, my conversation with God will return and the tiny fossils remind me of the beauty of creation.

OU MAY LIKE TO TRY MAKING YOUR OWN STAFF, DRIFTWOOD ISN'T ESSENTIAL, MBOO STICK OR DOWEL WILL DO, YOU WILL ALSO NEED SOME STRING OR YARN, RONG THREAD, A NEEDLE AND SOME ITEMS THAT REMIND YOU OF YOUR OWN TO PLACE... YOU COULD WRITE A FAVOURITE PRAYER ON A RIBBON, USE BEADS OLOURS THAT ARE SIGNIFICANT TO YOU, LAMINATE SMALL PHOTOS OF PEOPLE AND PLACES THAT ARE PRECIOUS TO YOU... (more on next page)

Wrap the yarn around one end of the stick to make a comfortable area to hold, if you are using driftwood or a found tree branch you may want to clean it up first; level the lower end, remove loose bark or sharp broken edges. I like to carve into split areas and embed bits of sea glass, shells or beach pottery. Anything you want to attach that isn't fabric will need a hole to thread through and you could also paint areas or glue things on.

PRAY WITH YOUR PILGRIM STAFF, USE THE ITEMS ON IT AS STARTING POINTS FOR YOUR PRAYERS.

CONSIDER IT AS A SUPPORT AND COMPANION, A TOOL THAT WHEN YOU HOLD IT MAKES YOU WANT TO TRAVEL FURTHER AND DEEPER INTO YOUR RELATIONSHIP WITH YOUR CREATOR.

JESUS REMEMBER ME

he INWARD pilgrimage

e tools you use are to help you focus, to guide your thoughts and
yers, you may also like to use some words to direct your journey
d help you discover more about your relationship with God.

LIGHT

ight in the darkness...

EN JESUS SPOKE AGAIN TO THE PEOPLE, HE SAID, "I AM THE LIGHT OF
HE WORLD. WHOEVER FOLLOWS ME WILL NEVER WALK IN DARKNESS,
BUT WILL HAVE THE LIGHT OF LIFE. JOHN 8:12

t does the light of Christ mean to you, is it
ething healing and life affirming or is it to be
ed because of the dark things it will expose?

LOVE

Love drives out fear...

AND SO WE KNOW AND RELY ON THE LOVE GOD HAS FOR US. GOD IS LOVE. WHOEVER LIVES IN LOVE LIVES IN GOD, AND GOD IN THEM. THIS IS HOW LOVE IS MADE COMPLETE AMONG US SO THAT WE WILL HAVE CONFIDENCE ON THE DAY OF JUDGMENT: IN THIS WORLD WE ARE LIKE JESUS. THERE NO FEAR IN LOVE. BUT PERFECT LOVE DRIVES OUT FEAR. 1 JOHN 4:16-18

So much of life is spoiled by fear. Fear of what might happen, fear of opinions of others, fear of rejection, fear of failure... is fear holding you back from living your life to the full? We all have the potential to fulfil God's will in our own unique way but potential is a delicate flower that needs nurturing with prayer, self-love and not a little discipline. How do you nurture your potential?

HOPE

Be joyful in hope...

T THIS HOPE BURST FORTH WITHIN YOU, RELEASING A CONTINUAL JOY. DON'T GIVE UP IN A TIME OF TROUBLE, BUT COMMUNICATE WITH GOD AT ALL TIMES. ROMANS 12:12

n life is challenging it can be really hard to feel joyful and when we
t can be swiftly followed by a feeling of guilt that there can be joy
happiness in the midst of difficulty. The hope that comes from God
ever is beyond any hope we can imagine, it fuels a deep joy that is
e likely to be expressed by a confidence in the future and a
dfast contentment that comes from constant conversation with God.
Sod to help you to recognise that deep joy within you.

The Flowing Tide

As you experiment more with prayer, and travel on your inward pilgrimage, you may find that you long to travel an external pilgrimage to a special location, do it if you can but go with the awareness that all pilgrimage will lead inwards, your heart and mind long to know their maker and understand how they fit in this vast universe. Travel knowing that God is speaking to you about that all th time and sometimes all we need to do is stop for a while and listen.

Psalm 130

Hints and tips for your inward Pilgrimage

Take time out. Just ten minutes a day or half an hour twice a week set aside purely for being in God's presence can make a big difference to how your spiritual life grows. Find a quiet place and give the time you have to God, you could use one of the prayers in this book.

Pray like it's as vital as breathing. Sometimes we place praying, like God, into box. We think God can only be met or talked to in Church or when a certa person is present, in reality we were created to communicate with our Creator, to enjoy a two-way conversation which never ends. There's so mu God wants to share with us, to show us and teach us, so pray constantly a be aware of Gods presence in all things.

Look for God in the small things. The snatched conversation you just had wit the shop assistant, God was there; the card you sent to a grieving friend, God was there; the moment you took to smell the flowers, God was there when you washed up after dinner, God was there. It isn't that God wants do the washing up for you or promise you that every washing up momen will be filled with joy but God may be telling you that if you spend those times that need little thought, in prayer and conversation with your Creator, then your life may be that bit richer and purposeful.

I should point out that if you don't pray during the washing up your life will not fall apart, I know that sometimes I'm so tired that I can't even form a coherent thought let alone pray sensibly and a few minutes of mindless washing up is a pleasurable chance to switch off. If you can't pr then try singing or humming and just be open to whatever God may wa to say to you.

Never 'beat yourself up' for not doing enough, practice just being and be available when God calls you to do something.

Allow yourself to be vulnerable to others and to God. It's not easy to do but when we allow others to see our true selves they will see more of God ar God will be able to use you more effectively to help others.